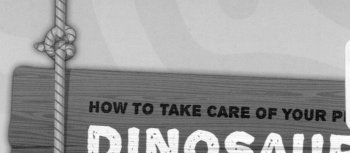

HOW TO TAKE CARE OF YOUR P[...]

DINOSAUR

YOUR PET
PLESIOSAUR

By Kirsty Holmes

THE
OFFICIAL
F.O.S.S.I.L
GUIDE

The Secret Book Company

King's Lynn
Norfolk PE30 4LS

ISBN: 978-1-91250-242-4

Printed in Malaysia

©This edition published in 2020. First published in 2019.

A catalogue record for this book is available from the British Library.

Written by:
Kirsty Holmes

Edited by:
John Wood

Designed by:
Danielle Jones

IMAGE CREDITS

CONTENTS

THE OFFICIAL FOSSIL GUIDE

Words that look like this can be found in the glossary on page 24.

F.O.S.S.I.L.

So – you're going to bring up a pet dinosaur. Congratulations!

Owning a pet dinosaur is a lot of hard work, but it's worth the trouble. Dinosaurs make excellent pets.

CONGRATULATIONS! IT'S A... PLESIOSAUR!

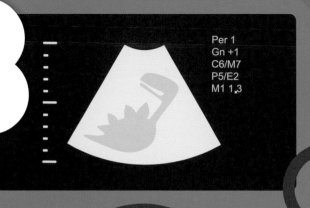

Per 1
Gn +1
C6/M7
P5/E2
M1 1,3

Plesiosaurs are not technically dinosaurs. They are actually marine lizards from the same <u>era</u> as the dinosaurs. Don't worry though – F.O.S.S.I.L. still has a book on how to take care of them.

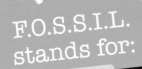

F.O.S.S.I.L. stands for:

Federal
Office of
Super
Sized
Interesting
Lizards

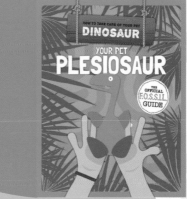

YOUR PET
PLESIOSAUR

PREGNANCY

Most Plesiosaur mothers don't lay eggs. Instead, they carry their babies inside them and give birth to live <u>young</u>. A pregnant Plesiosaur will need special care.

Plesiosaur mothers give birth to either one large baby, or up to three smaller babies.

PLESIOSAUR PARENTS WILL LOOK AFTER THEIR BABIES UNTIL THEY ARE READY TO LEAVE HOME.

BABIES

Plesiosaur babies can be different sizes, but at birth can be as large as two metres in length. This is around one-third of the mother's size!

BABIES ARE JUST LIKE SMALL VERSIONS OF THE ADULTS.

TWO METRES

SIX METRES

Baby Plesiosaurs like to live in shallow waters while they grow. If you are <u>rearing</u> your baby at home, you will need a large, warm, shallow pool.

FEED YOUR BABY PLESIOSAUR SMALL FISH AND SQUID.

GROWTH

Your Plesiosaur baby will grow very quickly. Depending on its exact <u>species</u>, a baby could grow to between 2 and 15 metres in length.

PLESIOSAURUS
THREE AND A HALF METRES

CRYPTOCLIDUS
FOUR METRES

ELASMOSAURUS
14 METRES

If your Plesiosaur turns out to be large, you must make sure you have a good place for it to live. If you live by the sea, your Plesiosaur can live there. If not, you will have to get creative.

FOOD

Plesiosaurs are <u>carnivores</u>. They have very sharp teeth and incredibly strong jaws, perfect for catching fish and other creatures.

SQUID – – →

MOLLUSCS

← – – FISH

CLAMS

SNAILS

Plesiosaurs are very good at catching and <u>digesting</u> their food. You will need to plan ahead to make sure you have enough food for it to eat every day.

EXERCISE

Your Plesiosaur will need plenty of exercise. If you want to go swimming with your Plesiosaur, you will need some good diving equipment.

F.O.S.S.I.L. FACT

Your Plesiosaur swims by flapping its flippers. Don't get slapped by a stray flipper!

Plesiosaurs can swim at around eight kilometres per hour.
This is pretty fast, so make sure you keep up with your swimming
lessons so you can keep up with your pet!

EIGHT
KILOMETRES PER
HOUR

NAMING

Naming your Plesiosaur is very important when <u>bonding</u> with your pet. You could choose a name that rhymes with 'Plesiosaur'.

Bessie-o-saur

F.O.S.S.I.L FACT

What will you name your Plesiosaur?

16

You could use a word that describes your Plesiosaur as its name. Plesiosaurs have big flippers, long necks and sharp teeth.

THIS OWNER NAMED HIS PET "FLIPPER" BECAUSE OF ITS FOUR BIG FLIPPERS.

FLIPPER!

WASHING

If your Plesiosaur lives in the sea, it will get covered with algae and barnacles. This won't win you first prize at any pet shows. To clean your Plesiosaur you will need:

A LADDER

A SCRAPING TOOL

A BROOM

LOTION

SOAP

You will need to lift your Plesiosaur out of the water to clean it. Make sure you remove anything stuck to its belly and apply some soothing lotion.

PROBLEMS

Plesiosaurs can swim a long way if kept in the ocean.
Consider fitting your Plesiosaur with a tracking device
so you can track its movements.

Plesiosaurs have small brains, so they aren't very clever. Teach your pet some simple commands – you'll need a megaphone to be heard across the sea.

TRICKS

Plesiosaurs are good at diving and often eat snails and small creatures from the bottom of the sea. Teach your pet to fetch!

FETCH!

Plesiosaurs are very friendly. Maybe you could meet up with other Plesiosaur owners and start a <u>synchronised swimming</u> team?

THERE ARE HOURS OF FUN TO BE HAD WITH YOUR FRIENDLY NEW PET!

GLOSSARY

BONDING	forming a close relationship
CARNIVORES	animals that eat other animals, rather than plants
DIGESTING	breaking down food into things that can be used by the body
ERA	a period of time in history
MOLLUSCS	creatures with soft bodies, no backbone and, usually, shells
REARING	to take care of a baby animal
SPECIES	a group of very similar animals or plants that can produce young together
SYNCHRONISED SWIMMING	a competitive sport where swimmers perform complex routines
YOUNG	an animal's offspring or babies

INDEX